Otis Doesn't Scratch

PCCS Books
Monmouth

First published 2015

PCCS Books Ltd
Wyastone Business Park
Wyastone Leys
Monmouth
NP25 3SR
UK
Tel +44 (0)1600 891 509
www.pccs-books.co.uk

Otis Doesn't Scratch

A CIP catalogue record for this book is available from the British Library.

This book constitutes part of ISBN 978 1 906254 56 8 – a two-part resource.

Cover designed by Raven Books based on an image by Tamsin Walker
Typeset by Raven Books
Printed by Alphaset, Surbiton, UK

My name is Ted.
I like football, fishfingers
and my friends –

and Otis. He's my cat.
He's orange and massive and kind.

I live with Mum.
Her real name is Mel
but to me she's just
Mum.

My mum's great, mostly.
We have good times, loads of them.
We put on our music THIS LOUD,
no,

LOUDER,

and we dance.
Mum looks like a crazy chicken. See?
She likes **really** bad music!

Some days we spend with
just each other.
We take sandwiches down by the lake

and lie back, watching.
The clouds are lazy,
the sky is deep.

We have bad times too
and we SHOUT.
Then it feels like I'm hurt on the inside,
squashed up tight like a fist.

Sometimes Mum gets sad
and she doesn't want to dance
– even with me.

It was that sort of day when I saw them –
the cuts on her arm. Four of them.
Like red mouths – open and scary.

I asked her,
'WHAT HAPPENED?'
She told me that Otis scratched her.

But Otis doesn't scratch. Not like that.

That's not all. Another time
there were bruises all up her leg.
Like bad fruit – purple and angry.

She said that she fell down the stairs,
but I would have heard that

– wouldn't I?

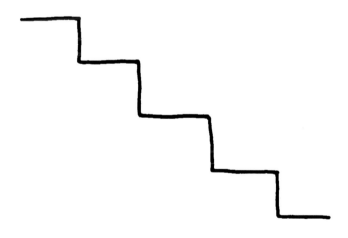

What had hurt her?
What had hurt my mum?

I had to find out.

So I grabbed Otis. He's hard to carry but
I put him up on the table
and stared straight at him.

He didn't like it one bit.
'Did you hurt my mum', I said.
'DID YOU SCRATCH HER?'

He got scared.
I didn't mean to shout.

Then he was gone –
out the cat flap – SLAP – like that.

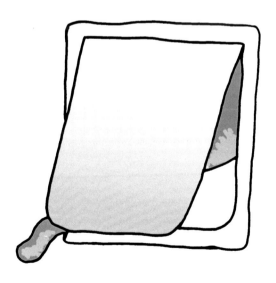

I was upset. I mean REALLY upset.
Worried about Otis –
but most of all, about my mum.

Had a bad man hurt her?
Was she ill?
Was Otis turning mean?

My thoughts were animals
inside my head.
They wouldn't stay still.
They wouldn't go to sleep.

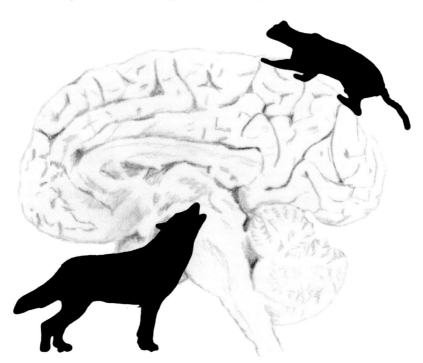

My head was heavy. My eyes hurt.
I didn't want to play with my mates,
or draw maps, or listen to stupid teachers
going BLAH BLAH BLAH.

I wanted to stop thinking.
I wanted to rest my head on the table
and sleep.

It was like I could sleep forever.
A sea with no seaside –
no sun.

That's when Mr Worston (my second-best teacher)
put his hand on my shoulder
and told me to stay behind.
He asked me what was the matter.

The
    t
       e
         a
           r
             s
                 came out
and they wouldn't stop.
I told him about Otis,
how he might never come back.

He might have been chased by a dog or been stolen
or run into a road and got hurt. He might be lost
with no one to take care of him, he'll be frightened
and all on his own.

Then I told him about my mum.

About the sad days, the cuts
and the bruises.
How scared I was.

Was it all my fault?
Was she going to die?

Mr Worston looked upset
in a kind sort of way.
He told me

he would do his very best to help,
and nothing – absolutely nothing –
was my fault. NOT AT ALL.

When I got home that night,
Mum said she wanted to speak to me.
Mr Worston had called.

I was sure she would be angry
or upset, or something.
But she wasn't.

She hugged me for a long time.
A hug like ... darkness – warm and deep.
Her breathing was like the sea.

She told me
it was her who did it.
She hurt her own arms,
her own legs.

I said,
'WHAT?
Not on purpose???'

And Mum just answered,
'Yes. She did it.
She hurt herself
when she felt really upset.

She said that mostly
she could find ways to make herself feel better –
like dancing, or talking to friends.

But some days were so bad
she didn't know
what else to do.

I said that was STUPID and CRAZY. Hurting yourself
is MAD.

Mum said it was hard to understand
but she would try to explain.

She said
some things made her feel so bad
the usual ways of helping herself
don't work.

Hurting herself
makes her feel better –
just for a bit.

I asked if she was ill.
She said that when she's really upset
it feels a lot like being ill.
But it isn't like getting a cold.
You can't catch it.

I asked Mum if she was going to die.
She squeezed me and said,
'No way!'
– like she really meant it.

I asked if hurting myself
would make me feel better.
Then she hugged me
for a long time. Tight.

She said she hoped I would never,
EVER,
need to hurt myself to feel better. She hoped
I would NEVER feel that bad.

We all get sad sometimes, or angry, or scared,
but there are loads of things I can do
to make myself feel better –
like asking for help, or dancing,

playing footie, or talking to my mates,
getting a hug or crying. Even crying
can make you feel better.

She said that whatever happens
I would always be her number one –
her sun.

She hoped I could always talk to her,
about anything,
no matter what.
She would do her best to help.

And if there was anything
I didn't want to talk about with her
then I could find someone else.

Someone I trust –
like Mr Worston, or my auntie,
or one of those phonelines
for kids who feel upset.

But there was a noise in my head
like a fire. I felt sick and hot,
and I shouted, 'But I want you to stop!
RIGHT NOW!'

Mum said she would try her very best.
She couldn't promise she would never do it again.
But she *could* promise to take care of herself

and ask people for help if she needed it,
to keep both of us, her and me,
safe and well.

Then she hugged me. This time she did cry
and so did I.
And it's true, I did feel better.

'So it wasn't Otis then?' I whispered,
and she answered,
'No. No it wasn't.'

'Hmmm', I said, and thought for a bit.
'I want you not to lie again.
And I want you to be happy. Always.'

But Mum told me, 'Sometimes we need to be sad.
And that way, we never forget
how wonderful it is to be happy.'

Otis Doesn't Scratch

Talking to young children about self-injury

PCCS Books
Monmouth

First published 2015

PCCS Books Ltd
Wyastone Business Park
Wyastone Leys
Monmouth
NP25 3SR
UK
Tel +44 (0)1600 891 509
www.pccs-books.co.uk

Otis Doesn't Scratch: Talking to young children about self-injury

A CIP catalogue record for this book is available from the British Library.

This book constitutes part of ISBN 978 1 906254 56 8 – a two-part resource.

Cover designed by Raven Books based on an image by Tamsin Walker
Typeset by Raven Books
Printed by Alphaset, Surbiton, UK

Introduction

I'm Clare. I wrote this guide to accompany *Otis Doesn't Scratch*, a storybook resource illustrated by Tamsin Walker.

Tamsin and I both work in mental health; and, of course, I'm a writer and she's an artist. But the main reason we came together to produce this resource was because we both have personal experiences of self-injury. Throughout the book, I'll draw from my own story to help you to make real-life sense of the issues we're addressing. Extracts from my own experiences appear in boxes.

I'm a teacher and a writer, and a mother. I also have a lengthy history of self-injury. Throughout my teenage years and well into my twenties, I used to cut myself and take overdoses. This meant I had a lot of contact with health services like A&E, and with mental health services including counsellors, psychiatrists and mental health nurses. I didn't always have a positive experience of services. Because of this, I became involved in trying to improve the way that services understand and respond to people who self-injure. I set up one of the UK's first self-injury support groups; I've written and edited articles, magazines and books on the issue; and I've delivered training courses in services across the UK and beyond. I'm also a poet. I have two poetry collections published with Bloodaxe (*Straight Ahead*, 2006; *Head On*, 2011) and I was described by the Arvon Foundation as 'one of Britain's most dynamic and powerful young poets'.

The idea for this resource emerged when I was facilitating a support group for people who self-injure. Most of the people in the group were parents; and most were struggling with questions like:

- Should I talk to my children about my self-injury?
- What should I say?
- How do I answer their questions?

We thought about some of the resources available to help younger children make sense of problems like cancer, diabetes and asthma, and how useful it would be to have something similar around self-injury. As my own daughter has grown older, I have also felt the need for some guidance.

Can you talk to children about self-injury?

Of course you can. Children, like adults, often live in difficult circumstances. Issues like poverty, disability, racism, loss, violence, illness and distress are everyday realities for some children. With the right resources and support, children are capable of making helpful sense of these issues. From *Oliver Twist* to *Grange Hill*, from *Tracy Beaker* to *War Horse*, books, films and television have succeeded in giving children the information they need to engage with challenging subjects. It may be scary, but talking about self-injury with children is possible. For some children, it's vital.

Should you talk to children about self-injury?

Self-injury – the act of intentionally hurting your body through, for example, cutting, burning or overdosing – is a common issue. It leads to over 200,000 attendances at Accident and Emergency departments each year, and it's one of the top five reasons for emergency admission to general hospital. Statistics suggest that three in every 100 people self-injure; in some groups, rates are even higher.

The reality is, many children and young people are affected by self-injury. They may hurt themselves, or they may have a friend, sibling, parent or close family member who self-injures. A child living with self-injury might feel scared, sad and alone. In the absence of the information they need to make sense of the issues they face, a child will make up their own explanations. And those explanations might be far more worrying and upsetting than the reality: 'Someone is hurting my Mum.' 'My Dad is going to die.' 'My sister is not okay and it's all my fault.'

We created this guide because of the confusion, negativity and fear that surround self-injury. We created it because of the lack of information and resources for younger children who are struggling with the issue. Most of all, we created it because we believe that talking helps.

How do you talk to children about self-injury?

The storybook resource that accompanies this guide is aimed at children aged four to eight who have a parent, guardian or close family member who self-injures. We have chosen to focus on this particular age group because of the lack of resources designed to meet their particular needs. You may feel that the resource is useful for older children. You may think it's helpful for children who harm themselves. You might find that it's useful just for yourself. In the Resources section you'll find suggestions of other sources of support and information.

The storybook uses illustrations and a simple story to engage children with some questions and some facts about self-injury, offering them age-appropriate information to help them make sense of the issue. Some children may take what they need from the story, others might want to have more in-depth conversations. This accompanying guide is designed to help you to have those conversations and to support children who are struggling with self-injury, giving you the information *you* need to make sense of it, and the confidence to support them to understand it too.

When might it be helpful to talk with a child about self-injury?
It might be useful:

- if they ask about it
- if someone close to them is self-injuring
- if you are concerned that they are injuring themselves
- if you've been asked to have the conversation by someone significant to the child, such as a parent
- if you have any other concerns relating to self-injury.

Talking about self-injury helps. No amount of information and support will make it an easy subject. But as much as it's about difficulty, *Otis Doesn't Scratch* is a story of love and hope. We hope you enjoy it. We hope you learn from it. Most of all, we hope it helps.

My daughter started to ask about my scars when she was around 18 months old: 'What are those stripes?'

I explained that they were scars. That was all she needed to know.

A few months later: 'What are scars?' I explained that they are the marks left behind when a cut gets better. That was enough.

More recently: 'How did you cut yourself?' 'Why were you so sad?' 'Did it hurt?' 'I don't want you to do it again.'

1. What is self-injury?

'… she told me it was her who did it.
She hurt her own arms,
her own legs.

I said, "WHAT? Not on purpose??"
and mum just answered, "Yes."'

The concept of self-harm

Imagine you're an alien. You've landed in an ordinary British town and you spend a few weeks watching people do the things that people usually do – at home, at work, at leisure. What examples might you see of people doing things that cause them harm?

You'd be likely to see people smoking, knowingly inhaling several thousand toxic chemicals. You'd almost certainly see people drinking too much alcohol, eating too much or too little, or eating the wrong kinds of food. You'd be bound to see people who didn't get enough exercise, seriously compromising every aspect of their physical wellbeing, alongside those who do too much exercise, or who engage in sports where injury is an accepted outcome. You'd see people with pierced and tattooed flesh, women in high heels causing severe discomfort and postural problems, people using wax and other methods to rip the hair from their bodies. You'd see people gambling or shopping themselves into serious debt; or people turning up day after day to unrewarding, stressful jobs, working shift hours or overtime; going without adequate sleep; not finding time for relaxation, hobbies or loved ones; relying on caffeine to keep them alert. The list could go on.

I bet you can look back over the last 24 hours and identify multiple ways you've caused harm to yourself …

So, let's abandon the idea that hurting yourself is a strange thing to do. Actually, every single one of us knows what it's like to cause harm to ourselves. This personal experience is a really helpful place to start to make sense of self-injury.

The term 'self-injury'

But when we use the term 'self-injury' we usually aren't referring to the huge spectrum of ways that people commonly cause harm to themselves. We're usually referring to something much more specific: 'hurting the self in order to cope with pain or numbness'.

Examples might include cutting, burning, scratching or hitting the self, or taking overdoses. You might have come across other examples – hair pulling, ingesting toxic substances, picking at skin or wounds, for example.

In *Otis Doesn't Scratch*, we've chosen to focus on cutting as it's one of the most common methods of self-injury. However, it's really important to acknowledge that there are lots of ways of causing injury to the self. It's also important to acknowledge that everyone's experience of self-injury will be different.

Some people may just use one method of self-injury – burning with cigarettes, for example. Others may hurts themselves in lots of different ways. Some people may injure themselves once or twice and not feel the need to repeat it. Others may self-injure over a period of months or even years. Some people may cause themselves severe harm; other people will self-injure in ways that pose much less risk to health or life. Some people may ask for help when they hurt themselves; others will go to extreme lengths to keep their injuries hidden. Particularly for those people who hurt themselves over long periods of time, patterns of self-injury may change.

I started to injure myself at the age of 10. At that age, and for the next few years, my self-injury was what you might call 'superficial'. By this I mean that I was inflicting small cuts on myself, which weren't enough for me to feel I needed medical attention. It certainly didn't mean that my distress or my need for support was 'superficial'.

I didn't tell anyone about my self-injury and I didn't receive any support. By the age of 15 I started to cut myself more deeply and frequently, and sometimes I would take overdoses. I was 20 when I first told someone. I continued to hurt myself for another 10 years.

At some points I was harming myself several times a day by cutting, overdosing and hitting myself, sometimes to a life-threatening degree. At the age of 26 I realised that I needed to change. I began to harm myself less frequently, and in less risky ways. By the age of 30 I found that I no longer needed to self-injure.

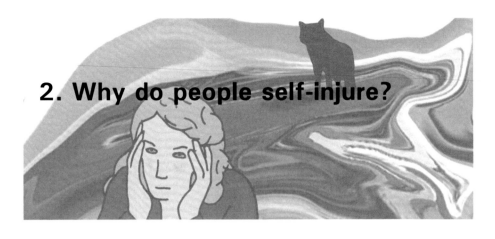

2. Why do people self-injure?

'Hurting herself makes her feel better – just for a bit.'

There are lots of different theories about why people self-injure. Some explanations are primarily physical or biological, others focus on individual psychological or emotional factors. Some explanations of self-injury will highlight social or environmental factors, like poverty or gender. Explanations can be contradictory and confusing – a brief internet search might uncover a range of ideas, for example, that self-injury is the result of opiate addiction; a symptom of personality disorder, impulse disorder or attachment disorder; an attempt at ego boundary differentiation; or a re-enactment of early trauma.

Don't worry. You don't need to read and get your head round all of these theories. In this resource, we will turn directly to what people who hurt themselves say about their self-injury.

In literature and research carried out by and with people who self-injure, there's a very clear message: people hurt themselves because it works. It is a way of surviving, preserving and affirming life in the presence of what is often experienced as intolerable distress.

> We all survive in different ways and if self-harm didn't serve a function then [we] wouldn't do it. (Walker, 2004, p. 21)

Experiences

Most people feel that their need to self-injure is related to experiences they have had. For many people, these experiences happened in childhood.

6

They often include:

- sexual abuse
- neglect
- emotional abuse
- lack of communication
- physical abuse
- loss/separation
- conflict and arguments
- other difficulties, for example, bullying.

Adult experiences can also be significant, particularly when they follow on from difficult experiences in childhood. They may include:

- rape/sexual abuse
- domestic violence
- lack of support/communication
- discrimination relating to sexuality, gender, ethnicity, ability
- other factors, for example, the break-up of a relationship, or admission to a secure setting such as a prison or psychiatric unit.

People who self-injure are likely to have struggled with painful issues in their lives – like exclusion, discrimination, isolation and trauma. We see high rates of self-injury amongst groups of people who are particularly vulnerable to these sorts of experiences, for example, children in the care system, asylum seekers, young women, homeless people, Asian women, young people who are unemployed.

> I believed that I was worthless and I assumed everyone else agreed. (NICE, 2011, p. 60)

Experiences like this can leave people struggling with some really difficult feelings. Particularly when we're not supported to deal with difficult issues, they can impact on how we make sense of ourselves and the people around us. Unsurprisingly, then, people who self-injure often report feeling high levels of distress prior to self-injury. Feelings may include:

- intense emotional pain: misery, sadness, grief, desperation or hopelessness
- self-hatred, guilt, shame, 'dirtiness', 'badness'
- anger and frustration, a sense of powerlessness
- anxiety, panic, fear, stress, tension
- feeling unsupported or unheard by others.

Some people also report feeling very cut-off, dissociated or numb before they self-injure. It might not be obvious to you what someone is struggling with, but one thing we do know is that if someone is feeling the need to hurt themselves, they are struggling in some way. Their struggle is real and valid, and it's important that they are not judged for it.

Self-injury and coping
The need to self-injure is rooted in difficult experiences and painful feelings. But that doesn't, in itself, explain why people hurt themselves. Doesn't causing injury and pain just make things worse?

Let's use your experiences as a starting point for making sense of self-injury. Think about how you deal with difficult emotions. What is it that you do to make yourself feel better? You might turn to wine, cigarettes, a visit to the gym, an hour of housework, a chat with a friend, comfort food. You might do something completely different. We all have strategies that help us to cope with difficult feelings.

Whatever coping strategy you have identified, now consider why you use it. What functions does it serve for you? Does it calm you down, or give you a feeling of relief or release? Does it give you a sense of control at those times when you feel powerless? Perhaps it works by distracting you and giving you a break from difficult feelings. Maybe it offers you a way of expressing your feelings or sharing your experiences with someone else. I'm guessing that the bottom line for most of us is that we use our chosen coping strategy because it works – it makes us feel better.

And the same is true for people who self-injure.

'She hurt herself
when she felt really upset.

She said that mostly
she could find ways to make herself feel better –
like dancing, or talking to friends.

But some days were so bad
she didn't know
what else to do.'

When people are asked to name the functions served by their self-injury, they name:

- To relieve feelings/improve mood:

  'Sometimes it makes me feel calm and … even though I'm hurting myself it sometimes makes me feel … good about myself.' (Heslop & Macauley, 2009, p. 54)

- To achieve a sense of control/power:

  'When things were happening to me that I had no control over I started hurting myself. This was something that I could control, I could do as much or as little damage as I wanted, it only involved myself. And I could care for the wound afterwards.' (National Self Harm Network, 2008, p. 3)

- To feel alive/connected:

  'When I feel numb and like I don't really exist, I cause my-self harm and it brings this rush that brings you back down to earth.' (Mental Health Foundation/Camelot Foundation, 2006, p. 25)

- To punish the self/resolve feelings of guilt and self-hatred:

  '… to take things out on myself, to drive the bad feelings away, punish myself for what I let happen to me, and to get the bad-ness out.' (National Self Harm Network, 2008, p. 3)

- To express distress and/or communicate a need for support:

  'It's a way of expressing negative feelings about myself that build up inside me. As someone who finds it difficult to put things into words, it can at times be the only way of expressing how I am feeling.' (National Self Harm Network, 2008, p. 3)

> I self-injured for at least 20 years of my life because it made me feel better. I would not have done it otherwise. It gave me a way of distracting myself from the intense distress I was in, a sense of release and relief as I let some of the bad feelings out.
>
> It was totally mine, and I knew it inside-out. No one could take it away from me, no matter what they did. Choosing when and how to injure myself gave me a feeling of control that I lacked in other areas of my life.
>
> It helped me to make sense of how I felt – making emotional pain real and visible in the form of physical injury. And by making it tangible, it gave me a way of communicating that pain to other people.

However ...

Whilst self-injury may be understood as a way of coping with painful feelings and experiences, it is also important to recognise that it is often associated with feelings of guilt and shame: 'most of the time I'm ashamed it's got to that' (Heslop & Macauley, 2009, p. 54).

> **trigger** (ˈtrɪɡ.ə(r))
>
> *n.*
>
> **1.** The lever pressed by the finger to discharge a firearm.
> **2.** An event that precipitates other events.

Understanding triggers

In the context of self-injury, a 'trigger' is the event or feeling that precipitates self-injury: the thing that happens immediately before someone needs to hurt themselves. Common triggers include arguments, financial problems, difficulties at work or at school, or witnessing someone else's self-injury. The trigger could also be 'a reminder of the past (such as an anniversary) which sets off a hidden memory' (Mind, 2010). Negative responses, comments and judgements relating to self-injury can be a powerful trigger for further harm. It can be helpful to understand the triggers that affect an individual so that:

- they can be avoided, if possible
- the person who self-injures can take measures to keep themselves safe
- greater levels of support can be offered when they are needed.

Identifying triggers, and making sense of the feelings and thoughts behind them, may also be part of the process of understanding self-injury. This can result in an improved sense of control and self-esteem for the person who self-injures, as well as giving staff and carers a better understanding of what might help.

But it's important to remember that there is a limit to what triggers can tell us. A trigger event – an argument, for example – might help us to understand why someone has felt the need to self-injure at a particular time. But it doesn't explain their feelings, or what they are thinking, or why self-injury is their chosen way of coping.

A trigger is the lever that fires the gun. That gun that is already loaded with difficult experiences, thoughts and feelings. It is very important that those deeper, more enduring issues are not overlooked or dismissed. As we have already acknowledged, many people point to childhood experiences as playing a pivotal role in their need to self-injure.

Finally, sometimes there is no single trigger – 'sometimes, ordinary life is just so difficult that self-harm is the only way to cope with it' (Mind, 2010, p. 7) – or triggers may be too personal and numerous to make sense of.

3. Self-injury and suicide

'I asked mum if she was going to die.
She squeezed my hand and said, "No way!"
– like she really meant it.'

One of the most common fears surrounding self-injury is the fear of suicide. It's understandable. Self-injury can be scary, especially if someone is in extreme distress, causing themselves severe harm, or expressing suicidal feelings. Sometimes, it can be hard to tell self-injury and suicide apart.

But for many people, self-injury is very different to suicide. It's about staying alive. It's a way of coping with difficult feelings and experiences, and it serves some powerful positive functions. For these people, self-injury is a way of coping. It may even be used as a way of surviving suicidal feelings.

> People often link self-harm to suicide but for me it was something different; it was my alternative to suicide, my way of coping even though sometimes I would wish that my world would end. (Mental Health Foundation/Camelot Foundation, 2006, p. 28)

Accordingly, the statistical relationship between self-injury and suicide is smaller than many people expect. Research indicates that around 0.7 per cent of people who are seen in hospital for self-injury will die by suicide (or self-inflicted injury) within a year of that self-injury. This figure increases to 2.4 per cent after 10 years (Hawton & Zahl, 2003). Statistically, the relationship between self-injury and suicide looks something like this:

If we think that someone is at imminent risk of suicide, we are likely to respond in quite drastic ways – by watching them constantly, for example, or removing anything they might use to hurt themselves with. If they are not at risk of suicide, these interventions are disproportionate, intrusive and controlling. Responding in this way to someone who is using self-injury as a way of coping may leave them feeling scared, angry and powerless. Even worse, it may remove their coping strategy at the time when they need it most.

However, it's important to acknowledge that there is an increased risk of suicide amongst people who self-injure. Following an act of self-injury the rate of suicide increases to between 50 to 100 times the rate of suicide in the general population (Hawton *et al.*, 2003).

At times, self-injury and suicide may be distinct. At other times, the issues may overlap. Somebody who self-injures may sometimes feel unclear about whether they want to live or die. 'You see, sometimes I want to kill myself but I don't, you know what I mean?' (Heslop & Macauley, 2009, p. 46). Where a person stands in relation to risk will change over time, sometimes within the space of a day.

We've already established that if someone is using self-injury as a way of coping, it's not helpful to treat them as though they are suicidal. But how do we make the distinction? How do we know if someone is suicidal?

How do I know if someone is suicidal?

Self-injury can indicate an increased risk of suicide. But not everyone who self-injures is suicidal. It is important to make a distinction between people who are self-injuring in order to cope and people who are at imminent risk of suicide.

The easiest way to check whether someone is feeling suicidal is to ask them about it. You will not make somebody feel more suicidal by simply raising the issue. On the contrary, you'll be giving them an opportunity to talk. This can be profoundly helpful.

> The most helpful people in my times of acute crisis were the ones
> I could call and ask for direct immediate help: talking for a long
> time on the telephone, providing company, a sleep-over, a video

or movie, holding me, cooking dinner for me. I gravitated towards those who were least judgemental and more open, because they felt safe. (Blauner, 2003, p. 62)

Sometimes, people don't feel able or don't want to name the fact that they are feeling suicidal. Other signs that somebody who self-injures is at risk include:

- Feelings of hopelessness: Not seeing a way forward, expressing opinions like, 'What's the point?'
- A recent negative life-changing event such as ber-eavement, job loss or a diagnosis of illness.
- Feelings of failure and loss of self-esteem: 'I'm no good for anything or anyone.'
- Talking about methods of suicide, having a plan or having access to the means of suicide.
- Taking less care of themselves than they usually do.
- Putting their affairs in order: Suddenly making a will, giving away possessions, returning borrowed items.
- Talking about suicide: It's a myth that people who talk about suicide don't go through with it. In fact, most people who have taken their own lives have spoken about it first.
- A marked change of behaviour: Some people may withdraw from friends, family and usual interests. Others may appear to be calm or happy for the first time. Without any obvious cause for these feelings, this may be an indication that they have decided to end their lives.
- Previous attempts: Someone who has thought about or attempted suicide in the past is more likely to respond in the same way when life becomes too painful.
- Hints that they 'won't be around'.

Suicidal thoughts and fantasies, alongside severe self-injury, had formed such an important part of my life for so long it's very hard to categorically state when suicide became the only option. What …

… I do remember is that even at the time I was aware of a qualitative difference in how I felt. I fully intended to bring about my own death. In previous attempts, when I'd taken overdoses or cut the arteries in my arms, I'd known that death was a possible outcome of my actions, but primarily, what I'd wanted was change – a change in my circumstances, in the way that people viewed me, in the way that I felt.

This time, there was no ambiguity. I wanted out, completely – complete escape into nothingness, total elimination of me. All other routes were now blocked. There was no other way forward. I felt strangely calm, at times, elated and euphoric. I stopped self-injuring. There was no longer any point.

If you think that someone is at risk of ending their life through suicide or self-injury, you must take immediate steps to keep that person safe.

- Take them seriously.
- Offer support.
- Treat them with respect and kindness.
- Persuade them to get help: from services listed below, from their GP, from services they may already be in contact with, and from personal support networks.
- In an emergency, call 999.
- Take care of yourself.

Barbara knew immediately that my cry for help was real … she told me not to do anything, just stay there and she was on her way round, now … Poor Barb, she didn't really know what to do. But she knew how to just be there for me, which is probably the most important thing of all. (Webb, 2010, p. 15)

Information and support

If you'd like some more support and information about suicide, we have listed some organisations and resources below.

Papyrus: www.papyrus-uk.org
Helpline: 0800 068 41 41
Helpline for young people struggling with distress and suicidal feelings, alongside resources and support for those dealing with suicide and emotional distress in teenagers and young adults.

Samaritans: www.samaritans.org
Helpline: 08457 90 90 90
Confidential support for those in despair or distress, alongside support and information for those who may be concerned about someone else.

Mind: www.mind.org.uk
Helpline: 0300 123 33 93 (9am–6pm Monday to Friday)
Advice and support for people struggling with mental health problems; and the people who support them.

CALM (Campaign Against Living Miserably): www.thecalmzone.net
Helpline: 0800 58 58 58 (5pm–midnight)
Support and resources for men experiencing depression and distress; aimed at preventing male suicide.

Survivors of Bereavement by Suicide: www.sobs.admin.care4free.net
Helpline: 0300 111 5065 (9am–9pm every day)
National helpline and other support services run by a self-help group for people bereaved by suicide. Helpline provides listening support and will put people in touch with their nearest local group.

4. Common assumptions about self-injury

'I said that was STUPID and CRAZY. Hurting yourself is MAD.'

The fact that someone self-injures tells us that they are having a hard time and may need a little extra kindness or support. But it tells us nothing about what somebody has been through and what they are feeling. It tells us very little about where they stand in relation to risk. It does not tell us about their particular reasons for self-injuring, or about what sort of person they are. It tells us nothing about their strengths, skills and qualities.

It is rarely helpful to assume that we know what is going on for someone. Unfortunately, self-injury is surrounded by assumptions. Hurting yourself is Mad. People who self-injure are Stupid and Crazy. People who hurt themselves are Bad Parents. Negative assumptions such as these are particularly unhelpful. Which is why, in this section, we address some of the most commonly held unhelpful assumptions about self-injury.

1. Self-injury is attention seeking.

> Some people do it for attention ... that doesn't mean they should be ignored. There are plenty of ways to get attention, why cause yourself pain? And if someone's crying for help, you should give them it, not stand there and judge the way they're asking for it. (Mental Health Foundation/Camelot Foundation, 2006, p. 27)

For many people, self-injury is an intensely personal act with personal functions. It may have nothing to do with wanting the attention of others. For other people, self-injury may be about communicating distress and seeking support.

17

From having someone to listen, someone to help us, or just someone to make us feel good, we all need attention. It's part of the human condition. The fact that someone is physically hurting themselves as a means of communicating their need for attention or support should alert us to just how great their need is.

However, the term 'attention seeking' is often used in a judgemental or dismissive way: 'It's just attention seeking, so the best response is to ignore it.' There are other ways to describe someone's self-injury that lead to a more helpful response, such as 'seeking support' or 'communicating distress'.

2. People who self-injure are manipulative.

For many people, self-injury is an intensely personal act with personal functions. It is much more likely to be about trying to cope with difficult feelings than trying to manipulate others.

However, in situations where people feel powerless or have limited access to other resources, self-injury might be used as a way of trying to impact on or change circumstances. There are times that many of us will have used emotive strategies such as crying or withdrawing in order to bring about a change in our circumstances, or to get a response from the people around us, particularly if we feel that we are unlikely to be listened to or have our needs met any other way. Words like 'manipulative' are a judgemental way of describing this process, and an unhelpful way of dismissing the needs and feelings of someone who self-injures.

3. It's only a scratch, nothing serious.

There is no direct correlation between the severity of someone's self-injury and the degree of distress they are feeling. Someone who self-injures by scratching themselves, for example, may be just as distressed as someone who inflicts very severe lacerations. You cannot infer levels of distress by simply looking at the injury. By doing this, you may actually encourage someone to injure themselves more severely if they feel that it is the only way of having their distress taken seriously.

4. People who self-injure are mentally ill/personality disordered.

Self-injury is not a psychiatric disorder, and many people who self-injure do not meet the criteria for psychiatric diagnosis.

Diagnosis tells us very little about an individual; it does not tell us about what a person has been through, how they feel about themselves or how they make sense of things. Diagnosis does not tell us about their reasons for self-injuring. Self-injury is more helpfully understood as a way of coping with difficult thoughts, feelings and experiences.

5. It's just learned/copycat behaviour.

'I asked if hurting myself
would make me feel better.
Then she hugged me for a long time. Tight.'

Some explanations of self-injury focus on the assumption that people engage in self-injury because they have seen other people doing it. It is sometimes assumed that a person may acquire the 'habit' simply by being in close proximity with someone who self-injures. According to this approach, self-injury is a sort of contagion – even reading information about self-injury, or looking at images, may be enough to prompt someone to do it (e.g. Walsh, 2008; Walsh & Rosen, 1989).

There is plenty of evidence that rates of self-injury are particularly high in closed/residential settings such as prisons, children's homes, boarding schools and psychiatric hospitals. Whilst research suggests that some people may have a prior history of self-injury, it also shows that others begin to injure themselves after they have entered these settings. This, alongside evidence of high rates of self-injury in certain friendship groups and subcultures – for example, 'emos' and 'goths' – is often offered in support of the theory that self-injury may be copied or 'caught'.

The contagion/copycat theory of self-injury will be of particular concern for anyone supporting a child who is exposed to self-injury. One of the most powerful fears for adults supporting a child in this situation is that the child may begin to self-injure too.

'She said that when she's really upset
it feels a lot like being ill.
But it isn't like getting a cold.
You can't catch it.'

Unravelling the myth of contagion

Yet as we have already addressed, people self-injure for powerful reasons – to cope with distressing thoughts, feelings and events. People do not start to self-injure simply because they know that someone else does.

With this in mind, we can return to the high rates of self-injury in children's homes, for example, and consider the powerful reasons that a young person might start to self-injure in those settings, including the early experiences of abuse and other trauma they are likely to have been through, and the disrupted attachments, bullying, discrimination and other difficult experiences they are likely to encounter in the care system. We can revisit the scenario of a woman who begins to self-injure after entering prison and explain it in terms of factors such as trying to cope with the distress caused by separation from friends and family, an attempt to protect herself from bullying, or trying to fit in. We can explain high rates of self-injury in the goth/emo subculture as the result of young people feeling drawn towards others with whom they feel a sense of identity.

> There is no statistical evidence to suggest that children with parents or close family members who self-injure are any more likely to hurt themselves.

However, in the National Inquiry (Mental Health Foundation/Camelot Foundation, 2006), young people reported the self-injury of someone close to them as one of the issues that led them to start hurting themselves. This is unlikely to be the result of children simply imitating self-injuring behaviours. It is more likely to be the result of:

- feeling worried, scared and upset by the self-injury
- having no one to talk to about the self-injury
- not receiving any support or information about self-injury
- viewing self-injury as a normalised and acceptable way of coping with feelings
- feeling that emotional and physical needs can only be met through self-injury
- unresolved issues that may run alongside the self-injury.

Just because a child is close to someone who self-injures, it does not mean they will begin to self-injure. However, it does mean that they may struggle with some difficult issues, feelings and questions about self-injury – which this book is designed to address.

Having a mother with extensive scarring caused by self-injury isn't always easy for my daughter. I'm aware that my history of self-injury has an impact on her, and that it's important I help her with this by talking about it, giving her appropriate information, and helping her to understand and manage her own feelings. I'm also aware that the impact of my history isn't all bad. My scars also tell her that mental health is an issue for all of us, that people go through bad times and come out of them again, that everyone is different and that difference is a positive thing, that you don't have to hide the fact that you're struggling, that it's important to be proud of who you are.

5. Self-injury and recovery

'But I want you to stop!
RIGHT NOW!'

Earlier in this guide, you were asked to identify the coping strategies you turn to at times of difficulty and distress. Return to that thought. Imagine someone telling you to stop. No wine, no cigarettes, no chat with a friend, no comfort food, no television. In this situation you might feel angry, upset, trapped, powerless. In short, you would probably feel a lot worse. And you might react by arguing, shouting, crying, withdrawing – or doing it anyway. Some of you might react by using your coping strategy even more – having two glasses of wine, two bars of chocolate, turning the music up, staying in the bath even longer.

Now apply this to self-injury.

Self-injury worries, upsets or scares us. Like Otis, we want it to STOP. We may ask someone not to do it again; we may hide the sharp things; we may threaten them with negative consequences. In services, people may be subject to 'no harm contracts'; they may face exclusion or withdrawal of support if they self-injure; they may be medicated, hospitalised, observed, even physically restrained.

But, as we've just identified, trying to stop someone from using their coping strategy at the time of greatest need is unlikely to be the most helpful response. It is likely to worsen feelings of distress; it may even lead to an increase in self-injury.

This guide is informed by a recovery approach to mental health. Implicit in this approach to mental health is the acceptance that recovery is a unique and individual process. For many people who self-injure, recovery may involve reaching a point where they no longer need or want to self-injure. For others, it may be about learning to live more safely and constructively. Most frequently, it is about good relationships, financial security, satisfying work, personal growth, the right living environment, finding meaning in difficult experiences, and the development of cultural or spiritual perspectives.

Most importantly, recovery is about hope. Things can and do get better.

> I did cut a couple of times in the month or two after I stopped cutting daily, but my therapist helped me not to panic or see it as slipping backwards, it was just what happened on the odd day that was worse than the rest. Yes, I still think about it every now and then. It's a bit like quitting smoking. The temptation will always be there, and I accept that. But I'm lucky … I've got my life back. And I'm going to hang on to it with all the strength I've got. ('Pippa' in Baker *et al.*, 2013, p. 68)

Even whilst someone is continuing to self-injure, individuals and services can play an important role in showing concern for the distress that underlies the self-injury: offering help with addressing practical and emotional problems, and supporting them to keep themselves, and their children, safe and well. The rest of this guide will describe how that might happen, and what support and resources you might need.

> I couldn't tell you the last time I self-injured because I didn't know it was going to be the last time. I stopped hurting myself because the need to do it gradually went away. My life got better; I got decent support from services; I had people around me who cared for me; and I changed. I wanted a life worth living, and I wanted to be happy. Having hurt myself as a way of coping for over half of my life, it took me some time to get to the point where I didn't need it anymore.

6. Responding to self-injury

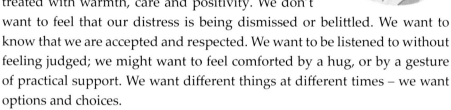

If trying to prevent self-injury isn't the most helpful response, what is? Back to you.

When you're going through a difficult time in your life, how do you want to be responded to?

It seems safe to guess that most of us want to be treated with warmth, care and positivity. We don't want to feel that our distress is being dismissed or belittled. We want to know that we are accepted and respected. We want to be listened to without feeling judged; we might want to feel comforted by a hug, or by a gesture of practical support. We want different things at different times – we want options and choices.

That's exactly what people who self-injure want. Positive attitudes, alongside information and involvement, are the most important determinants of whether a response will be helpful (RCP, 2007).

It isn't necessary to be highly qualified or experienced to respond helpfully to self-injury. Responding to someone with warmth and respect – acknowledging their difficulties, whilst offering reassurance and acceptance – will make a real difference.

For more information about resources that may support you in working with, or supporting someone who self-injures, see the Resources section.

Supporting parents who self-injure

A parent who self-injures may have particular support needs, such as an extra need for reassurance that you will not judge them as a parent on the basis of self-injury alone. Given the profound negativity that surrounds self-injury, there is an understandable basis to these fears.

> I have lived with self-injury – and the scars of self-injury – all of my adult life, and I've experienced a lot of negative reactions as a result. Since I got pregnant, I have been more aware than ever of the negative judgements that people might make about me. I'm afraid that they will assume I'm not a good parent. It makes it hard for me to be open about my self-injury; I feel self-conscious; and sometimes it really affects my confidence as a parent.

In the following sections, we'll identify questions of risk and harm which may arise when you are supporting a parent who self-injures. It is also important to recognise their strengths and qualities, including the positive ways they may have managed their self-injury.

It may be necessary for you to offer practical support around parenting, or to offer information about where this support can be accessed, alongside some extra help for the individual to access this support given some of the obstacles they may face. It may be helpful to assist them with making contact with other parents who are struggling with these issues. It will certainly be important for the parent to feel that they are able to talk openly and honestly with you or another appropriate adult about self-injury.

A child or young person is never an appropriate source of support. It is not their responsibility to take care of their parent, friend or family member.

Some people make ill-informed, negative assumptions about me as a parent with a history of self-injury and a diagnosis of borderline personality disorder. But I've also had some very positive experiences. My therapist has been supportive since I first started planning a family – I've always felt that she sees me as a good mother. I found pregnancy and the first months of parenthood very difficult, and her support was particularly important to me then. I was open about my history and my diagnosis with my health visitor; this led to a short discussion in which she explained that I might be at higher risk of developing postnatal depression. She checked out whether I and the people around me would know if I was getting depressed, and what to do in that case. She left me feeling that I could ask for help if I needed to, because I wasn't scared of being judged. The message she left me with was that motherhood is really difficult for most of us, but for some of us there are extra challenges. It's okay to ask for help, and it's important that help is freely available if we need it.

7. Harm minimisation for self-injury

'She couldn't promise she would never do it again.
But she could promise to take care of herself
and ask people for help if she needed it
to keep both of us – her and me –
safe and well.'

As we have recognised, most of us cause harm to ourselves through everyday behaviours like overwork and unhealthy eating. It's striking to notice that the risks involved in some common behaviours, like smoking and drinking, can potentially be more severe that those involved in some forms of self-injury.

We've also recognised that self-injury, like any other coping strategy, serves some important positive functions: people do it because it makes them feel better!

But it is also important to acknowledge that self-injury comes with costs. In this next section we will address the risks and damage involved in self-injury, and look at how these might be minimised.

In previous sections, we recognised that people who self-injure may sometimes have suicidal thoughts and feelings. Where there are real concerns that someone is at imminent risk of suicide, it is appropriate to take immediate action to prevent this. This may include inviting someone to talk with you, contacting services, staying with someone, or removing implements or substances that a person may use to harm themselves whilst they are in crisis.

However, most people self-injure as a way of coping with difficult feelings and experiences. In these circumstances, preventative measures like these are not appropriate or helpful. They may even lead to an increase in risk and harm.

During my 20 years of self-injury, I had several admissions to psychiatric units. Self-injury 'wasn't allowed' in these places. If you self-injured, you could have your medications increased. You might be placed on constant observations; you'd lose your access to the gym or occupational therapy. Home visits and leave would be cancelled; discharge would be delayed. As a direct result, my self-injury became much more risky and severe. I had to do it secretly. I had to use whatever I could find to hurt myself with, and I had to do it as quickly as I could before I was stopped. Because I knew I'd be in trouble if I told anyone, I'd keep my injuries hidden, even when it was obvious I needed medical attention.

Consider responding to self-injury from a harm minimisation approach. You may be more familiar with this in the field of substance misuse, where common examples include needle exchange schemes and education campaigns like 'Talk to Frank'. Projects like this aim to reduce infections and overdose, and to give people the information they need to make informed choices about their actions.

In the 1980s, the message about drug use was 'just say no'. It didn't work! People carried on using street drugs anyway. Harm minimisation is based on the acceptance that people will take street drugs whether we like it or not, and that it makes more sense to help them do so in a safer way – to reduce the cost to them and the people around them.

How can this approach be applied to self-injury? As The Basement Project puts it:

Just because you hurt yourself doesn't mean that your safety and your health don't matter. You do matter. That's why it's important to keep the damage to the minimum. You deserve to take the best care of yourself you can, while you're self-injuring. (The Basement Project, n.d.)

No matter how much we might want someone to stop hurting him or herself, and no matter how well they are being supported, someone who has been using self-injuring as a way of coping is unlikely to give up overnight. In these circumstances, it's really helpful for the person to be supported to keep themselves – and the people around them – as safe as possible when they self-injure.

The sort of information, resources and support that might help Ted's mum to keep safe include:

- basic anatomical information so that she knows the dangers and consequences of cutting or hitting herself
- how to recognise when she needs medical attention, and how to go about getting it
- advice about keeping wounds clean, to reduce risk of infection
- signs of infection, and how to respond to them
- first aid supplies, and how to use them
- advice about tetanus and other jabs and boosters
- information about what services are available to support her
- help to understand the reasons why she self-injures, including triggers
- reassurance that she is not being judged as a person or as a parent.

> When I was self-injuring, I had no idea about things like nerves, tendons and arteries. So it came as shock to me when I cut through them. I'm a violin player, a rock-climber, a writer. I didn't want to lose the use of my hands. Once I'd realised the risks, I started to take some simple steps to reduce them, like not cutting so deeply and taking better care of myself after I'd self-injured. This didn't just help me to keep safe; it also left me feeling better about myself. I felt more positive about my body, less shame about my self-injury and an increased sense of control within my own life.

Resources for reducing risk

For more ideas about practical strategies for reducing risk and damage, see the downloadable resources listed below. These focus on reducing the physical risks for someone who self-injures but the same principles can be extended to cover the potential negative impact on other people. In the next section we shall consider what this means in practice, with particular reference to children.

The following are available to download free of charge from: www.kreativeinterventions.com

The Hurt Yourself Less Workbook
A practical tool which aims to enable people who self-injure to keep themselves as safe as possible. It includes lots of practical exercises devised by people who self-injure, and a useful section on self-injury and hearing voices.

Cutting the Risk: Self-harm, self-care and risk-reduction
A practical and informative book, written by people who self-injure for people who self-injure, with detailed advice on how to minimise the risks involved in self-injuring.

8. Minimising the harm for others

Harm minimisation isn't just about maximising the safety of the person who self-injures. It's also about the people around them. When someone is hurting themselves, the people around them might be hurt too.

Physical risks include:

- risk of infection from blood spillage
- risk of injury if sharps (e.g. blades) are not stored or disposed of safely
- risk of overdose if medication or toxic substances are left unattended
- risk of fire if open flames or flammable substances are involved.

Children and other dependants may face additional physical risks, such as the risk of neglect if a parent is too distressed or physically incapacitated to care for them.

Even more common is the risk of emotional harm and distress caused to those who care for someone who self-injures. Research conducted with clinicians and practitioners shows that very powerful feelings can be evoked by self-injury. The emotions frequently named by staff include: shock, horror and disgust, incomprehension, fear and anxiety, distress and sadness, anger and frustration, powerlessness and inadequacy, futility and responsibility (e.g. Duperouzel & Fish, 2007).

The emotional impact on family, friends, partners and, crucially, children, is likely to be even more marked.

'My thoughts were animals
inside my head.
They wouldn't stay still.
They wouldn't go to sleep.'

It is vital that a child's emotional and physical safety is taken seriously. If someone self-injures, it does not mean that they are not a good parent. But it does mean that steps must be taken to reduce the potential negative impact of that self-injury on a child. In the next section, we consider what those steps may be.

9. Safeguarding

If you are a parent who self-injures, there are some really powerful things you can do to keep your child safe and well.

If you feel at risk of self-injury, draw up a plan that you can turn to when you are feeling really distressed. Your plan should include:

- how to access support when you need it
- a list of trusted people and services you find helpful to talk to when you are very distressed
- how to take care of yourself emotionally and physically when in severe distress
- how you want others to take care of you.

Informed by the issues addressed in this chapter, identify the risks your child might be exposed to if you self-injure. Think through how you will reduce these risks. Include this in your plan.

You may want to draw from the guidelines below.

If you self-injure

DO:

- Store blades and medication safely away from the reach of children. Make sure that blades and medications etc. are replaced in a safe place after you have self-injured.
- Keep wounds and injuries appropriately dressed and covered. Not only does this reduce the risk of infection, it also reduces the distress caused by the sight of a fresh injury.
- Seek medical attention when necessary.
- Be aware of your physical and emotional needs, and commit yourself to meeting them as far as possible.
- Clear up thoroughly after yourself so that children are not exposed to, for example, blood spillage.

DON'T:

- Self-injure when you are on your own with a child/children. It may leave you unable to care for them and it increases the risk that they will witness your self-injury.

- Use an open flame to burn yourself.
- Self-injure in front of children. This is always emotionally damaging and physically risky for your child; there is never a good reason for this to happen.
- Run the risk of your child/children finding you if it goes wrong. Always have access to medical attention, for example, by being within easy reach of a phone.
- Tell your child/children that self-injury is okay. Whilst it's important that your child knows that self-injury doesn't mean you are mad, out of control or about to die, it's also important that they don't learn that self-injury is a positive option.

> 'Why did you cut yourself?' she asks.
>
> 'Because I was really unhappy, and I thought it might help me to feel better. I didn't know what else to do.'
>
> 'Did it help?'
>
> 'It made me feel a bit better for a little while. But in the end it didn't really help. I had to find other ways of making things better for myself.'
>
> 'What like?'
>
> 'Oh, talking to people – friends and stuff.'

Being a good parent doesn't mean being perfect all the time. It involves asking for help when you need it. Sometimes, it involves making mistakes – and learning from them. It involves having the strength to admit your needs and vulnerabilities, and the willingness to address them.

You matter, very much. But your child's safety must be a priority.

Be aware and honest about your capacity to look after your child. If your levels of emotional distress or physical injury/illness are preventing you from being able to keep them safe and well, ask for help. Draw up a 'safe list' of trusted people who can help. You might want to talk to other people who self-injure about services you can use and trust. Use the support that is available to you.

In an emergency, call **999**.

10. Child protection

What if you have concerns about a child's safety?

The vast majority of parents who self-injure are entirely capable of protecting their child's physical and emotional welfare – particularly if they have access to the information and support we've suggested.

The fact that a parent self-injures does not, in itself, mean that a child is at risk.

However, self-injury may be a child protection issue if:

- a parent isn't keeping the child physically and emotionally safe around their self-injury
- the parent is actively suicidal
- the self-injury means that a parent isn't physically able to care for the child, for example, they are hospitalised or otherwise incapacitated
- the parent lacks a network of support
- the self-injury is indicative of other unresolved problems, such as severe mental distress, domestic violence or substance misuse
- the child is experiencing significant difficulties as a result of the self-injury or associated issues
- the child is failing to thrive
- you have any concerns that the child is being physically, emotionally or sexually maltreated.

If you suspect that a child is being placed at risk, neglected or harmed, you *must* take action. Contact the social care department provided by the council in your area who are available 24 hours a day to discuss your concerns. You can find your council's contact details online at www.gov.uk/find-your-local-council or in the phonebook.

If you are working with a parent or child in a professional capacity and have significant concerns about their safety, refer to your organisational Child Protection Policies and Procedures and raise your concerns with your supervisor and manager.

If your concerns are urgent and you suspect that a child is at imminent risk of harm, call 999.

11. How to talk to children about self-injury

"'Hmmm," I said, and thought for a bit.
"I want you not to lie again."'

Self-injury is a tough subject. It brings up all sorts of difficult feelings – sadness, fear, anger. It raises difficult questions, and painful issues. Talking about self-injury with a young child can be a scary prospect. Sometimes, it's easier to avoid it.

But difficult things happen and we have to deal with them. So do children. When we avoid talking about difficult issues with kids, we can cause them more worry and distress, and we miss the opportunity to give them the information and support they may need. If we are going to help them to deal with difficult things, we have to let them know that it's okay to talk about them. It might not feel okay for us, but we're the adults, and it's up to us to manage that.

So, don't avoid the subject. If the child isn't asking, don't presume that's because they don't need to know. A child may be expressing their questions, their confusion or their feelings in other ways – for example, through their play or their behaviour. Be open to other ways of communicating with the child, like drawing and storytelling.

The storybook resource *Otis Doesn't Scratch* has been designed to offer children simple, accessible information about self-injury in pictures and words. You might want to read the book with the child and open up a conversation in this way. This guide is intended to give the information and confidence you need to talk with them about the story and any questions it raises.

Be aware of your limits … make sure you are the right person to have this conversation. If this falls outside the remit of your personal or professional relationship with the child, there may be someone else more appropriate. If you are close to the child or the parent, be aware of the issues and the emotions that this raises for you. If you are feeling overwhelmed, there may be someone more appropriate you can ask to have the conversation.

If you are going to talk with the child, start by finding out what they know. Get a sense of what their fears and concerns are, and if they have any misconceptions or particular questions. Be guided by them in providing the information, understanding and comfort they need.

> 'Then I told him about my mum.
> About the sad days, the cuts
> and the bruises.
> How scared I was.
>
> Was it all my fault?
> Was she going to die?'

Make sure that the information you offer is appropriate to the child's age and development. Keep your answers brief and simple. Unnecessary details will confuse or overwhelm them.

You might plan a conversation with a child; more often, you'll find that it happens spontaneously. It might be prompted by something on the television, a situation at home, a conversation at school ... Conversations might be full of emotion, or they might be brief and informal. Be guided by the child, what they want to talk about, and how. Don't impose your expectations and agenda. Let them decide.

Be aware of time and place – make sure it's appropriate for the child.

Talk at the pace that the child sets: let them break off and talk about other things. They will let you know when they have done talking – and it may be very quickly! Be prepared to have lots of smaller conversations rather than one long one. Often, a child will take time to think about an issue and come back at a later point with more questions. Children usually need to ask the same question several times. Every question deserves a thoughtful answer. As a child grows older, they will return to the issue with different questions, ideas and feelings.

Ask the child questions too, for example: 'How do you feel?' 'What do you think?' Feedback from the child will give you a sense of what they have understood, and how they feel about it.

Be aware of the child's emotions … no matter how gentle the conversation is it will bring up difficult feelings for the child. These need to be acknowledged and responded to. Be reassuring: address the child's worries; let them know that they are not on their own, that things can and will get better, and that support is available. Be honest; don't make promises you can't keep.

'He told me

he would do his very best to help,
and that nothing – absolutely nothing –
was my fault. Not at all.'

Be aware of your own emotions. Self-injury is likely to bring up difficult feelings and issues for you – don't let these impact negatively on your conversation with the child. They need to feel safe with you, and to be confident that you are okay, present and engaged in the conversation.

Make sure that the child's concerns about self-injury don't mask other issues or anxieties – be aware of, and alert to, what else might be going on for the child.

Be prepared to talk again. And again.

And again …

'Then she hugged me. This time she did cry
and so did I.
And it's true, I did feel better.'

12. Mental health matters

*'Sometimes we need to be sad.
And that way, we never forget
how wonderful it is to be happy.'*

'Mental health' is not a medical condition. It describes how we think and feel about ourselves, other people and the world around us. It describes our ability to cope with life's difficulties and to learn from the experiences we have.

We all have the capacity for good – or poor – mental health. One in three people will develop a diagnosable mental illness at some point in their lives. Whether it's about protecting our mental and emotional wellbeing, coping with mental health problems when they arise, or taking care of the people around us, mental health is everyone's issue.

Being mentally healthy does not mean being happy all the time. Sometimes it's more appropriate to feel sad, angry or scared. Facing difficult events and difficult feelings is an inevitable part of life. We can't change our genetic make-up; we can't solve social problems like poverty overnight; we will all, at some point, experience loss and conflict; some of us will face trauma and other horrible experiences. The following things can help children and adults to face difficult experiences:

- positive, helpful ways of thinking
- safe environments and relationships
- supportive networks within families, schools and communities
- opportunities to talk openly and be listened to
- positive choices, options and information
- care and affection. (Mental Health Foundation, 1999)

Parental difficulties can have a negative impact on children. It's important that a child is reassured that, in difficult circumstances, it is normal and understandable to feel worried, angry, scared or upset. Learning to recognise and express emotions is an important ingredient of mental health.

We have considered how children may be supported and protected around self-injury. In the final section we will acknowledge how you, as a concerned adult, can take care of yourself.

13. The emotional impact of self-injury

*'My head was heavy. My eyes hurt.
I didn't want to play with my mates.'*

Self-injury is an emotive issue. Worry, fear, guilt, shock, grief and anger – the difficult feelings caused by self-injury can have a significant effect on the mental and physical wellbeing of friends, family, carers and professionals who support someone who self-injures.

Staff working with people who self-injure should be well supported by their organisations, in order to protect their professional practice and their individual wellbeing (NICE, 2004, 2011). They should have access to training, supervision, management and team support, and clear policies and guidelines.

If you are supporting someone in an informal capacity, it may be less clear where to go to for support. But support is still important. It is vital that you take your own physical and emotional wellbeing seriously, and seek support whenever you need it. The emotional impact on relatives, friends, partners and carers of people can be particularly acute:

> You tend to blame yourself ... I wasn't watching, I wasn't caring enough, I wasn't showing enough love.' (MacDonald *et al.*, 2007, p. 303)

It may be helpful to create a list of trusted people and services. In the resources section of this guide, you'll find a list of organisations and services who may be able to offer support and information, including information about carers' support groups, and a formal carer's assessment (NICE, 2011).

*'We all get sad sometimes, or angry, or scared,
but there are loads of things I can do
to make myself feel better –
like asking for help, or dancing.'*

Finally, it is also really important that you take care of yourself. That means asking for help when you need it. It also means taking care of your own needs. Be alert to physical needs. Consider the ways you help or harm yourself through:

- diet
- exercise
- sleep
- substance use, including alcohol, cigarettes and caffeine.

Consider how you look after your emotional needs – or not – in terms of:

- relationships
- work
- relaxation/hobbies
- how you express your feelings and needs.

All of us, whether we self-injure or not, have the capacity to harm ourselves or care for ourselves. All of us have the capacity to suffer and struggle. What matters is how we face those struggles.

14. And finally …

Both Tamsin and I have faced horrible experiences and difficult times in our lives. Our scars are evidence of that. Nothing can take away the pain of horrible experiences; and nothing can make self-injury into a simple or easy issue. Life hurts sometimes, and no matter how much you might want to, you can't change that.

But you can help.

Whenever you respond to someone in distress with respect and compassion, you help. When you offer comfort, information and understanding to a child struggling with a difficult issue, you help.

This guide has explained how self-injury is just one way that people make sense of and cope with their difficulties. It has described how people who self-injure – like all of us – should be treated with respect, acceptance and compassion.

It has explored how the risks and difficulties associated with self-injury can be minimised, and kept within the parameters of acceptable risk and safety. It has emphasised the shared responsibility of all adults to ensure the physical and emotional safety and wellbeing of all children, and the obligation to act when children are at risk.

It has acknowledged that self-injury, particularly when children are involved, can be a difficult and emotional issue to deal with. It has given you the information you need to understand self-injury and how to respond helpfully, and the confidence you need to have supportive, informed conversations with children who are living with the issue.

Thank you for reading this book. We hope – we really hope – it helps.

'And that's how we both feel now.
Sometimes sad,
but mostly happy.
And that's okay.'

Resources:
Support and information for self-injury

'… if there was anything
I didn't want to talk about with her
then I could find someone else.

Someone I trust –
like Mr Worston, or my auntie,
or one of those phonelines
for kids who feel upset.'

Helplines and websites

Childline:
www.childline.org.uk
Helpline: 0800 1111
24-hour service for children and young people up to the age of 19.

Samaritans:
www.samaritans.org
Helpline: 08457 90 90 90
24-hour support for those in despair or distress.

Self injury Support (formerly Bristol Crisis Service for Women):
www.selfinjurysupport.org.uk
Helpline: 0808 800 8088
A national service that supports girls and women who self-injure; offering a telephone helpline as well as text and email support, along with a range of informative publications on self-injury and related issues.
TESS text support for girls and young women who self-injure: 0780 047 2908

Papyrus:
www.papyrus-uk.org
Helpline: 0800 068 41 41
Support and resources – including publications and training – for those dealing with suicide and emotional distress in teenagers and young adults.

CALM (Campaign Against Living Miserably):
www.thecalmzone.net
Helpline: 0800 58 58 58 (5pm–midnight)
Support and resources for men experiencing depression and distress.

Carers Trust:
www.carers.org
Support, information and resources for carers.

Mind:
www.mind.org.uk
Helpline: 0300 123 33 93 (9am–6pm Monday to Friday)
Advice and support for people struggling with mental health problems, and the people who support them.

NSHN (National Self Harm Network):
www.nshn.co.uk
A survivor-led organisation with a range of information about self-injury and an online support forum.

The Basement Project:
https://basementprojectbooks.wordpress.com
Information and publications about self-injury and related issues.

The Site:
www.thesite.org/healthandwellbeing/mentalhealth/selfharm
Advice, support and information for young people on all aspects of self-injury.

Recommended publications

Arnold, L., & Magill, A. (2005). *The Self-harm Help Book.* Abergavenny: The Basement Project.

Arnold, L., & Magill, A. (2005). *What's the Harm? A book for young people who self-harm.* Abergavenny: The Basement Project.

Arnold, L., & Magill, A. (2005). *Working with Self-injury.* Abergavenny: The Basement Project.

Hanworth, K., Rodham, K., & Evans, E. (2005). *Youth and Self-harm: Perspectives.* Oxford: Samaritans & Centre for Suicide Research, University of Oxford.

Heslop, P., & Macauley, F. (2009). *Hidden Pain? Self-injury and people with learning disabilities.* Bristol: Bristol Crisis Service for Women.

LifeSIGNS (2004). *Self Injury Awareness Booklet: Information for health care workers, family and friends and teachers of people who harm themselves* (2nd edition). Available at: www.lifesigns.org.uk/files/lifesigns-si-awareness-book-2nd-edition-revised.pdf (Accessed January 2015).

Mental Health Foundation/Camelot Foundation (2006). *Truth Hurts: Report of the National Inquiry into self-harm amongst young people.* London: Mental Health Foundation/Camelot Foundation.

Newham Asian Women's Project (2007). *Painful Secrets: A qualitative study into the reasons why young Asian women self-injure.* Newham: Newham Asian Women's Project.

Pembroke, L. (1994). *Self-harm: Perspectives from personal experience.* London: Survivors Speak Out.

Richardson, C. (2006). *The Truth About Self-harm for Young People and Their Friends and Families.* London: Mental Health Foundation/Camelot Foundation.

Shaw, C., Biley, F., & Baker, C. (Eds) (2013). *Our Encounters with Self-harm.* Ross-on-Wye: PCCS Books.

Warner, S., & Spandler, H. (Eds) (2006). *Beyond Fear and Control: Working with young people who self-harm.* Ross-on-Wye: PCCS Books.

Warner, S., Spandler, H., & Shaw, C. (Eds) (2013). Minimising Harm, Maximising Hope: A special edition of 'Asylum – the magazine for democratic psychiatry'.

References

Baker, C., Biley, F., & Shaw, C. (Eds). (2013). *Our Encounters With Self-harm*. Ross-on-Wye: PCCS Books.

Blauner, S. (2003). *How I Stayed Alive When my Brain was Trying to Kill Me*. New York: HarperCollins.

Duperouzel, H., & Fish, R. (2007). Why couldn't I stop her? Self injury: The views of staff and clients in a medium secure unit. *British Journal of Learning Disabilities, 36*(1), 59–65.

Hawton, K., Harriss, L., Hall, S., Simkin, S., Bale, E., & Bond, A. (2003). Deliberate self-harm in Oxford, 1990–2000: A time of change in patient characteristics. *Psychological Medicine, 33*(6), 987–995.

Hawton, K., Zahl, D., & Weatherall, R. (2003). Suicide following deliberate self-injury: Long-term follow-up of patients who presented to a general hospital. *British Journal of Psychiatry, 182*, 537–542.

Heslop, P., & Macauley, F. (2009). *Hidden Pain? Self-injury and people with learning disabilities.* Bristol: Bristol Crisis Service for Women.

MacDonald, G., O'Brien, L., & Jackson, D. (2007). Guilt and shame: Experiences of parents of self-injuring adolescents. *Journal of Child Health Care, 11*, 298–310.

Mental Health Foundation (1999). *Bright Futures: Promoting children and young people's mental health*. London: Mental Health Foundation.

Mental Health Foundation/Camelot Foundation (2006). *Truth Hurts: Report of the National Inquiry into self-harm amongst young people*. London: Mental Health Foundation/Camelot Foundation.

Mind (2010). *Understanding Self-harm*. London: Mind.

National Institute for Health and Clinical Excellence (NICE) (2004). *Self-injury: The short term physical and psychological management and secondary prevention of intentional self-harm in primary and secondary care*. London: NICE.

National Institute for Health and Clinical Excellence (2011). *Self-injury: Longer term management*. London: NICE.

National Self Harm Network (2008). *What is Self Harm?* Available at: www.nshn.co.uk/downloads/What_is_self_harm.pdf (Accessed January 2015).

Royal College of Psychiatrists (2007). *Better Services for People Who Self-injure: Quality standards for healthcare professionals*. London: Royal College of Psychiatrists.

Shaw, C. (2006). *Straight Ahead*. Hexham: Bloodaxe.

Shaw, C. (2011). *Head On*. Hexham: Bloodaxe.

The Basement Project (n.d.). *Self-harm: Staying safe* [leaflet]. Abergavenny: The Basement Project.

Walker, T. (2004). Why cut up? *Asylum, 14*(3), 21.

Walsh, B. (2008). *Treating Self-injury: A practical guide*. New York: Guilford Press.

Walsh, B., & Rosen, P. (1989). *Self-mutilation: Theory, research, and treatment*. New York: Guilford Press.

Webb, D. (2010). *Thinking About Suicide: Contemplating and comprehending the urge to die*. Ross-on-Wye: PCCS Books.